REVISE KEY STAGE 2 SATs
Mathematics

TARGETED PRACTICE ARITHMETIC

Series Consultant: Janice Pimm

Authors: Christopher Bishop and Brian Speed

- -

Also available:

Revise Mathematics Key Stage 2 SATs Targeted Practice
Geometry, Measures and Statistics   9781292146225

Revise Mathematics Key Stage 2 SATs Targeted Practice
Number, Ratio and Algebra   9781292146232

For the full range of Pearson revision titles, visit:
www.pearsonschools.co.uk/revise

Contents

A small bit of small print

The Standards and Testing Agency publishes Sample Test Materials on its website. This is the official content and this book should be used in conjunction with it. The questions in this book have been written to help you practise what you have learned in your revision. Remember: the real test questions may not look like this.

Introduction

About your tests

At the end of Year 6, you will take tests to find out about your maths skills. This book will help you revise your **arithmetic** skills.

- There will be one **arithmetic** test. This test will ask you to carry out calculations. You will have 30 minutes to do this test.

- You will also need to use your arithmetic skills in the two **reasoning** tests. These tests will ask you to solve problems. You will have 40 minutes to do each test.

Using this book

Each page of this book is about a different maths skill. Use the checkboxes at the top of the page to track your progress:

Had a go ☐ Tick this box when you've read the page.

Nearly there ☐ Tick this box when you understand the page quite well.

Nailed it! ☐ Tick this box when you understand the page really well.

Written addition 1

Do your working in the spaces and write your answers in the boxes.

> Make sure you line up the digits in the columns correctly.

1. 38 + 26 =

```
    3 8
 +  2 6
 ─────
    6 4
    ₁
```

64

1 mark

2. 93 + 99 =

1 mark

3. 132 + 65 =

1 mark

4. 246 + 67 =

1 mark

5. 289 + 123 =

1 mark

6. 373 + 195 =

1 mark

7. 456 + 324 =

1 mark

8. 564 + 198 =

1 mark

Written addition 2

Do your working in the spaces and write your answers in the boxes.

Use estimation to check your answers.

1. 478 + 299 =

2. 566 + 486 =

1 mark

1 mark

3. 568 + 632 =

4. 678 + 524 =

1 mark

1 mark

5. 1,456 + 2,971 =

6. 3,745 + 2,983 =

1 mark

1 mark

7. 13,145 + 3,732 =

8. 24,562 + 7,852 =

1 mark

1 mark

2

Written subtraction 1

Do your working in the spaces and write your answers in the boxes.

> Make sure you line up the digits in the columns correctly.

1. 56 – 17 =

$$\begin{array}{r} {}^{4}\cancel{5}{}^{1}6 \\ -\ 1\ 7 \\ \hline 3\ 9 \end{array}$$

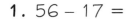

2. 63 – 29 =

39

1 mark

1 mark

3. 85 – 37 =

4. 94 – 69 =

1 mark

1 mark

5. 754 – 126 =

6. 862 – 235 =

1 mark

1 mark

7. 789 – 598 =

8. 1,987 – 727 =

1 mark

1 mark

Written subtraction 2

Do your working in the spaces and write your answers in the boxes.

Take care to line the numbers up in the correct columns.

1. 4,529 – 134 =

```
  4 ⁴5̶ ¹2 9
–     1 3 4
  4 3 9 5
```

4,395

1 mark

2. 3,762 – 568 =

1 mark

3. 5,694 – 299 =

1 mark

4. 7,567 – 478 =

1 mark

5. 2,768 – 1,106 =

1 mark

6. 5,769 – 2,198 =

1 mark

7. 8,695 – 3,459 =

1 mark

8. 18,754 – 1,099 =

1 mark

Multiplying by 10, 100 and 1,000

Do your working in the spaces and write your answers in the boxes.

To multiply by 10, 100 or 1,000, move the digits left by one, two or three places.

1. $17 \times 10 =$

```
 1   7
1  7  0
```

170

1 mark

2. $756 \times 10 =$

1 mark

3. $7,689 \times 1,000 =$

1 mark

4. $549 \times 1,000 =$

1 mark

5. $8,549 \times 10 =$

1 mark

6. $6,064 \times 1,000 =$

1 mark

7. $345 \times 1,000 =$

1 mark

8. $648 \times 1,000 =$

1 mark

Short multiplication 1

Do your working in the spaces and write your answers in the boxes.

Write the numbers in columns and multiply each place value in turn.

1. 13 × 6 =

```
    1 3
  ×   6
  -----
    7 8
    1
```

78

1 mark

2. 54 × 7 =

1 mark

3. 89 × 9 =

1 mark

4. 342 × 4 =

1 mark

5. 456 × 5 =

1 mark

6. 457 × 6 =

1 mark

7. 783 × 8 =

1 mark

8. 299 × 5 =

1 mark

Short multiplication 2

Do your working in the spaces and write your answers in the boxes.

Work from right to left. Leave space to carry numbers.

1. 1,678 × 3 =

```
    1 6 7 8
×         3
    5 0 3 4
    2 2 2
```

5,034

1 mark

2. 2,678 × 5 =

1 mark

3. 9,872 × 8 =

1 mark

4. 3,425 × 7 =

1 mark

5. 8,739 × 8 =

1 mark

6. 7,343 × 5 =

1 mark

7. 6,984 × 4 =

1 mark

8. 5,432 × 6 =

1 mark

Long multiplication 1

Do your working in the spaces and write your answers in the boxes.

Multiply each digit in the first number by each digit in the second number. Then add your answers together.

1. 22 × 12 =

```
      2 2
  ×   1 2
  -------
    2 2 0
      4 4
  -------
    2 6 4
```

264

2 marks

2. 43 × 24 =

2 marks

3. 56 × 38 =

2 marks

4. 134 × 23 =

2 marks

5. 278 × 37 =

2 marks

6. 435 × 67 =

2 marks

8

Long multiplication 2

Do your working in the spaces and write your answers in the boxes.

1. 2,345 × 21 =

```
      2 3 4 5
  ×       2 1
    4 6 9¹0 0
      2 3 4 5
    4 9 2 4 5
        1
```

49,245

2 marks

2. 3,879 × 24 =

2 marks

3. 4,632 × 36 =

2 marks

4. 7,862 × 45 =

2 marks

5. 6,732 × 56 =

2 marks

6. 2,768 × 63 =

2 marks

Dividing by 10, 100 and 1,000

Do your working in the spaces and write your answers in the boxes.

To divide by 10, 100 or 1,000, move the digits one, two or three places to the right.

1. 40 ÷ 10 =

4   0
 ↘ ↘
  4 . 0

4

1 mark

2. 300 ÷ 100 =

1 mark

3. 1,400 ÷ 100 =

1 mark

4. 7,000 ÷ 1,000 =

1 mark

5. 2,500 ÷ 100 =

1 mark

6. 3,200 ÷ 10 =

1 mark

7. 1,720 ÷ 10 =

1 mark

8. 100 ÷ 100 =

1 mark

Short division

Do your working in the spaces and write your answers in the boxes.

> The number you are dividing by always goes on the left of the calculation.

1. 72 ÷ 3 =

```
  2 4
3)7 ¹2
```

24

1 mark

2. 295 ÷ 5 =

1 mark

3. 438 ÷ 6 =

1 mark

4. 927 ÷ 9 =

1 mark

5. 528 ÷ 4 =

1 mark

6. 84 ÷ 7 =

1 mark

7. 364 ÷ 7 =

1 mark

8. 864 ÷ 8 =

1 mark

Short division with remainders

Do your working in the spaces and write your answers in the boxes.

Remember to include the remainder in the answer box.

1. $62 \div 3 =$

```
    2 0 r 2
  -------
3 | 6 2
```

20 r 2

1 mark

2. $86 \div 5 =$

1 mark

3. $86 \div 6 =$

1 mark

4. $916 \div 9 =$

1 mark

5. $575 \div 9 =$

1 mark

6. $57 \div 4 =$

1 mark

7. $577 \div 8 =$

1 mark

8. $917 \div 8 =$

1 mark

Long division

Do your working in the spaces and write your answers in the boxes.

If you cannot fit any lots of the divisor in the first two numbers, look at all three numbers.

1. 156 ÷ 13 =

```
        1 2
  13 | 1 5 6
      1 3 0   (13 × 10)
      ─────
        2 6
        2 6   (13 × 2)
      ─────
          0
```

12

2 marks

2. 165 ÷ 15 =

2 marks

3. 576 ÷ 18 =

2 marks

4. 345 ÷ 23 =

2 marks

5. 405 ÷ 27 =

2 marks

6. 527 ÷ 31 =

2 marks

Long division with remainders

Do your working in the spaces and write your answers in the boxes.

> Remember to include the remainder in the answer box.

1. 169 ÷ 14 =

```
        1 2 r 1
   14 | 1 6 9
        1 4 0      (14 × 10)
          2 9
          2 8      (14 × 2)
            1
```

12 r 1

2 marks

2. 165 ÷ 16 =

2 marks

3. 408 ÷ 19 =

2 marks

4. 3,146 ÷ 21 =

2 marks

5. 3,415 ÷ 28 =

2 marks

6. 5,537 ÷ 33 =

2 marks

Squares and cubes

Do your working in the spaces and write your answers in the boxes.

1. a) $3^2 =$

   $3^2 = 3 \times 3$

   $\quad = 9$

9

   1 mark

   b) $7^2 =$

   1 mark

   c) $8^2 =$

   1 mark

   d) $11^2 =$

   1 mark

   e) $9^2 =$

   1 mark

   f) $12^2 = .$

   1 mark

2. a) $2^3 =$

   $2^3 = 2 \times 2 \times 2$

   $\quad = 4 \times 2$

   $\quad = 8$

8

   1 mark

   b) $3^3 =$

   1 mark

   c) $9^3 =$

   1 mark

   d) $6^3 =$

   1 mark

3. a) $2^3 \times 3^2 =$

   1 mark

   b) $4^3 - 4^2 =$

   1 mark

Mixed operations

Do your working in the spaces and write your answers in the boxes.

> Do calculations in brackets first, then multiplication and division, then addition and subtraction.

1. a) $10 + 5 - 3 =$

$15 - 3 = 12$

12

1 mark

b) $8 + 2 - 4 =$

1 mark

2. a) $5 + 2 \times 3 =$

1 mark

b) $(5 + 2) \times 3 =$

1 mark

3. a) $20 - 5 \times 3 =$

1 mark

b) $(20 - 5) \times 3 =$

1 mark

4. a) $12 \div 4 - 1 =$

1 mark

b) $12 \div (4 - 1) =$

1 mark

5. a) $16 + 8 \div 2 =$

1 mark

b) $(16 + 8) \div 2 =$

1 mark

Adding decimals 1

Do your working in the spaces and write your answers in the boxes.

> Line up the decimal places in columns and add as you would for whole numbers.

1. 6.2 + 7.8 =

```
    6 . 2
 +  7 . 8
 ─────────
 1 4 . 0
     1
```

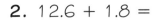

14

1 mark

2. 12.6 + 1.8 =

1 mark

3. 15.9 + 5.7 =

1 mark

4. 23.4 + 10.7 =

1 mark

5. 26.5 + 11.8 =

1 mark

6. 32.6 + 19.4 =

1 mark

7. 52.5 + 36.7 =

1 mark

8. 12.3 + 42.9 =

1 mark

Adding decimals 2

Do your working in the spaces and write your answers in the boxes.

Line up the digits carefully! Where do the decimal points go?

1. 34.06 + 51.4 =

```
  3 4 . 0 6
+ 5 1 . 4 0
  8 5 . 4 6
```

85.46

1 mark

2. 265.6 + 55.04 =

1 mark

3. 722.58 + 129.08 =

1 mark

4. 24.05 + 67.8 =

1 mark

5. 87.09 + 113.02 =

1 mark

6. 327.50 + 20.14 =

1 mark

7. 248.34 + 0.4 + 12.68 =

1 mark

8. 562.6 + 0.66 =

1 mark

Subtracting decimals 1

Do your working in the spaces and write your answers in the boxes.

> Line up the digits by place value and subtract as you would for whole numbers.

1. 9.5 – 1.2 =

```
  9 . 5
- 1 . 2
  8 . 3
```

8.3

1 mark

2. 6.35 – 2.71 =

1 mark

3. 4.05 – 1.2 =

1 mark

4. 34.23 – 15.08 =

1 mark

5. 16.72 – 12.78 =

1 mark

6. 84.56 – 37.05 =

1 mark

7. 89.78 – 56.45 =

1 mark

8. 66.66 – 17.77 =

1 mark

Subtracting decimals 2

Do your working in the spaces and write your answers in the boxes.

1. 72.05 − 13.02 =

$$\begin{array}{r} {}^{6}\!\!\not{7}{}^{1}\!2.05 \\ -\ 13.02 \\ \hline 59.03 \end{array}$$

59.03

1 mark

2. 37.06 − 12.03 =

1 mark

3. 27.43 − 11.22 =

1 mark

4. 56.97 − 40.08 =

1 mark

5. 64.08 − 34.76 =

1 mark

6. 59.87 − 14.07 =

1 mark

7. 89.32 − 15.34 =

1 mark

8. 43.87 − 32.89 =

1 mark

Multiplying decimals by 10, 100 and 1,000

Do your working in the spaces and write your answers in the boxes.

> To multiply by 10, 100 or 1,000, move the digits left by one, two or three places.

1. $0.75 \times 10 =$

$$0 . 7 \; 5$$
$$7 . 5 \; 0$$

7.5

1 mark

2. $0.75 \times 1,000 =$

1 mark

3. $1.56 \times 1,000 =$

1 mark

4. $9.52 \times 10 =$

1 mark

5. $9.52 \times 100 =$

1 mark

6. $9.52 \times 1,000 =$

1 mark

7. $67.32 \times 100 =$

1 mark

8. $51.02 \times 100 =$

1 mark

Multiplying with decimals 1

Do your working in the spaces and write your answers in the boxes.

Multiply the decimal by 10, 100 or 1,000, to get a whole number. Remember to divide by 10, 100 or 1,000 at the end.

1. 0.5 × 3 =

    0.5 × 10 = 5

       5 × 3 = 15

     15 ÷ 10 = 1.5

1.5

1 mark

2. 4.67 × 6 =

1 mark

3. 7.98 × 7 =

1 mark

4. 8.67 × 9 =

1 mark

5. 8.05 × 8 =

1 mark

6. 8.23 × 5 =

1 mark

7. 5.57 × 8 =

1 mark

8. 6.78 × 9 =

1 mark

22

Multiplying with decimals 2

Do your working in the spaces and write your answers in the boxes.

> Use estimation to check your answer.

1. $0.5 \times 4 =$

$0.5 \times 10 = 5$

$5 \times 4 = 20$

$20 \div 10 = 2$

2

1 mark

2. $0.7 \times 7 =$

1 mark

3. $0.6 \times 8 =$

1 mark

4. $0.02 \times 3 =$

1 mark

5. $0.04 \times 3 =$

1 mark

6. $0.06 \times 2 =$

1 mark

7. $0.03 \times 7 =$

1 mark

8. $0.12 \times 2 =$

1 mark

Dividing by 10, 100 and 1,000 with decimals

Do your working in the spaces and write your answers in the boxes.

> To divide by 10, 100 or 1,000, move the digits right by one, two or three places.

1. 67 ÷ 10 =

6 7
↘ ↘
6.7

1 mark

2. 893 ÷ 1,000 =

1 mark

3. 12 ÷ 1,000 =

1 mark

4. 19.7 ÷ 10 =

1 mark

5. 8.5 ÷ 100 =

1 mark

6. 98,950 ÷ 1,000 =

1 mark

7. 65.2 ÷ 100 =

1 mark

8. 40.2 ÷ 10 =

1 mark

Dividing with decimal answers 1

Do your working in the spaces and write your answers in the boxes.

Remember to write the decimal point in your answer.

1. 13 ÷ 2 =

$$\begin{array}{r} 6\,.\,5 \\ 2\overline{\smash{)}1\,3\,.\,{}^1 0} \end{array}$$

6.5

1 mark

2. 17 ÷ 4 =

1 mark

3. 147 ÷ 6 =

$$\begin{array}{r} 2\,4\,.\,5 \\ 6\overline{\smash{)}1\,4^2 7\,.\,{}^3 0} \end{array}$$

24.5

1 mark

4. 66. ÷ 8 =

1 mark

5. 1,156 ÷ 5 =

1 mark

6. 164 ÷ 8 =

1 mark

7. 2,340 ÷ 8 =

1 mark

8. 8,582 ÷ 5 =

1 mark

Dividing with decimal answers 2

Do your working in the spaces and write your answers in the boxes.

> Add a decimal point and a zero to carry the remainder from the units.

1. 789 ÷ 6 =

$$
\begin{array}{r}
1\ 3\ 1\ .\ 5 \\
6\overline{)7^1 8\ 9\ .\ {}^30}
\end{array}
$$

131.5

1 mark

2. 723 ÷ 15 =

1 mark

3. 8,596 ÷ 35 =

1 mark

4. 4,860 ÷ 48 =

1 mark

5. 8,899 ÷ 44 =

1 mark

6. 2,695 ÷ 28 =

1 mark

Adding fractions

Do your working in the spaces and write your answers in the boxes.

> If the denominators are the same, you just need to add the numerators.

1. $\dfrac{3}{10} + \dfrac{4}{10} =$

$\dfrac{3 + 4}{10}$

$$\boxed{\dfrac{7}{10}}$$

1 mark

2. $\dfrac{1}{5} + \dfrac{2}{5} =$

1 mark

3. $\dfrac{2}{10} + \dfrac{3}{10} =$

1 mark

4. $\dfrac{2}{9} + \dfrac{1}{9} =$

1 mark

5. $\dfrac{1}{4} + \dfrac{3}{4} =$

1 mark

6. $\dfrac{3}{8} + \dfrac{1}{8} =$

1 mark

7. $\dfrac{5}{12} + \dfrac{5}{12} =$

1 mark

8. $\dfrac{1}{5} + \dfrac{4}{5} =$

1 mark

Adding fractions with different denominators

Do your working in the spaces and write your answers in the boxes.

> Change all of the fractions to have the same denominator.

1. $\frac{1}{4} + \frac{1}{2} =$

$$\frac{1}{2} = \frac{2}{4}$$

$$\frac{1}{4} + \frac{2}{4} = \frac{3}{4}$$

1 mark

2. $\frac{1}{3} + \frac{1}{6} =$

1 mark

3. $\frac{1}{5} + \frac{3}{10} =$

1 mark

4. $\frac{1}{4} + \frac{5}{12} =$

1 mark

5. $\frac{1}{3} + \frac{1}{5} =$

1 mark

6. $\frac{1}{8} + \frac{1}{3} =$

1 mark

7. $\frac{1}{2} + \frac{1}{5} =$

1 mark

8. $\frac{3}{5} + \frac{1}{3} =$

1 mark

Subtracting fractions

Do your working in the spaces and write your answers in the boxes.

> If the denominators are the same, you just need to subtract the numerators.

1. $\dfrac{7}{10} - \dfrac{4}{10} =$

$\dfrac{7-4}{10} = \dfrac{3}{10}$

$$\boxed{\dfrac{3}{10}}$$

1 mark

2. $\dfrac{4}{5} - \dfrac{2}{5} =$

1 mark

3. $\dfrac{7}{10} - \dfrac{3}{10} =$

1 mark

4. $\dfrac{5}{8} - \dfrac{1}{8} =$

1 mark

5. $\dfrac{8}{9} - \dfrac{2}{9} =$

1 mark

6. $\dfrac{9}{10} - \dfrac{3}{10} =$

1 mark

7. $\dfrac{11}{12} - \dfrac{9}{12} =$

1 mark

8. $\dfrac{4}{5} - \dfrac{3}{5} =$

1 mark

Subtracting fractions with different denominators

Do your working in the spaces and write your answers in the boxes.

Change both fractions to have the same denominator.
$\frac{1}{2}$ is the same as $\frac{2}{4}$

1. $\frac{1}{2} - \frac{1}{4} =$

$\frac{2}{4} - \frac{1}{4} = \frac{1}{4}$

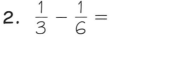

$\boxed{\dfrac{1}{4}}$

1 mark

2. $\frac{1}{3} - \frac{1}{6} =$

1 mark

3. $\frac{1}{2} - \frac{1}{5} =$

1 mark

4. $\frac{2}{3} - \frac{1}{5} =$

1 mark

5. $\frac{5}{8} - \frac{1}{5} =$

1 mark

6. $\frac{4}{5} - \frac{2}{3} =$

1 mark

7. $\frac{3}{4} - \frac{2}{3} =$

1 mark

8. $\frac{1}{2} - \frac{2}{5} =$

1 mark

30

Adding and subtracting with mixed numbers

Do your working in the spaces and write your answers in the boxes.

First convert mixed numbers to improper fractions, then find a common denominator.

1. $2\frac{1}{2} + \frac{1}{4} =$

$2\frac{1}{2} = \frac{10}{4}$

$\frac{10}{4} + \frac{1}{4} = \frac{11}{4}$

$$\boxed{\frac{11}{4} \text{ or } 2\frac{3}{4}}$$

1 mark

2. $3\frac{1}{3} + \frac{5}{6} =$

1 mark

3. $1\frac{5}{8} - \frac{1}{3} =$

$1\frac{5}{8} = \frac{13}{8} = \frac{39}{24}$

$\frac{1}{3} = \frac{8}{24}$

$\frac{39 - 8}{24} = \frac{31}{24}$

$$\boxed{\frac{31}{24} \text{ or } 1\frac{7}{24}}$$

1 mark

4. $3\frac{1}{2} - \frac{2}{5} =$

1 mark

5. $2\frac{3}{4} - \frac{1}{3} =$

1 mark

6. $1\frac{1}{2} + 1\frac{2}{5} =$

1 mark

31

Multiplying fractions 1

Do your working in the spaces and write your answers in the boxes.

> Multiply the numerator by the whole number.

1. $\frac{1}{2} \times 2 =$

$$\frac{1 \times 2}{2} = \frac{2}{2}$$
$$= 1$$

1

1 mark

2. $\frac{1}{3} \times 2 =$

1 mark

3. $\frac{3}{4} \times 4 =$

1 mark

4. $10 \times \frac{2}{5} =$

1 mark

5. $\frac{3}{5} \times 2 =$

1 mark

6. $2 \times \frac{5}{6} =$

1 mark

7. $\frac{5}{8} \times 4 =$

1 mark

8. $\frac{2}{3} \times 4 =$

1 mark

Multiplying fractions 2

Do your working in the spaces and write your answers in the boxes.

> Multiply the numerators together then multiply the denominators together.

1. $\frac{1}{4} \times \frac{1}{3} =$

$$\frac{1 \times 1}{4 \times 3} = \frac{1}{12}$$

$$\boxed{\frac{1}{12}}$$

1 mark

2. $\frac{4}{5} \times \frac{5}{6} =$

1 mark

3. $\frac{5}{8} \times \frac{1}{5} =$

1 mark

4. $\frac{3}{4} \times \frac{2}{5} =$

1 mark

5. $\frac{3}{8} \times \frac{4}{5} =$

1 mark

6. $\frac{7}{8} \times \frac{2}{5} =$

1 mark

7. $\frac{3}{5} \times \frac{5}{8} =$

1 mark

8. $\frac{3}{4} \times \frac{2}{3} =$

1 mark

Dividing fractions 1

Do your working in the spaces and write your answers in the boxes.

> When you divide fractions by whole numbers, only the denominator changes.

1. $\frac{1}{4} \div 3 =$

$$\frac{1}{4 \times 3} = \frac{1}{12}$$

$$\boxed{\frac{1}{12}}$$

1 mark

2. $\frac{1}{5} \div 3 =$

1 mark

3. $\frac{3}{8} \div 2 =$

1 mark

4. $\frac{3}{5} \div 4 =$

1 mark

5. $\frac{5}{6} \div 3 =$

1 mark

6. $\frac{5}{8} \div 3 =$

1 mark

7. $\frac{3}{4} \div 5 =$

1 mark

8. $\frac{2}{3} \div 5 =$

1 mark

34

Dividing fractions 2

Do your working in the spaces and write your answers in the boxes.

1. $\dfrac{1}{3} \div 10$

$$\dfrac{1}{3 \times 10} = \dfrac{1}{30}$$

$$\boxed{\dfrac{1}{30}}$$

1 mark

2. $\dfrac{4}{5} \div 10 =$

1 mark

3. $\dfrac{5}{8} \div 12 =$

1 mark

4. $\dfrac{3}{11} \div 3 =$

1 mark

5. $\dfrac{5}{8} \div 21 =$

1 mark

6. $\dfrac{3}{10} \div 24 =$

1 mark

7. $\dfrac{7}{8} \div 15 =$

1 mark

8. $\dfrac{7}{8} \div 47 =$

1 mark

Multiplying and dividing with mixed numbers

Do your working in the spaces and write your answers in the boxes.

> Change mixed numbers to improper fractions first.

1. $2\frac{1}{4} \times 3 =$

$2\frac{1}{4} = \frac{9}{4}$

$\frac{9}{4} \times 3 = \frac{27}{4}$

$$\boxed{\frac{27}{4} \text{ or } 6\frac{3}{4}}$$

1 mark

2. $3\frac{1}{3} \times 5 =$

$$\boxed{}$$

1 mark

3. $2\frac{3}{8} \div 2 =$

$$\boxed{}$$

1 mark

4. $1\frac{4}{5} \div 4 =$

$$\boxed{}$$

1 mark

5. $1\frac{3}{4} \times 6 =$

$$\boxed{}$$

1 mark

6. $2\frac{5}{8} \times 7 =$

$$\boxed{}$$

1 mark

Percentage amounts 1

Do your working in the spaces and write your answers in the boxes.

Use your knowledge of common percentages. Divide by 2 to find 50%.

1. 50% of 12 =

12 ÷ 2 = 6

6

1 mark

2. 10% of 60 =

1 mark

3. 20% of 30 =

1 mark

4. 75% of 36 =

1 mark

5. 30% of 40 =

1 mark

6. 5% of 80 =

1 mark

7. 80% of 50 =

1 mark

8. 40% of 90 =

1 mark

Percentage amounts 2

Do your working in the spaces and write your answers in the boxes.

Find three and a half lots of 10%.

1. 5% of 20 =

10% of 20 = 2 so 5% = 1

1 mark

2. 25% of 20 =

1 mark

3. 5% of 60 =

1 mark

4. 15% of 60 =

1 mark

5. 5% of 80 =

1 mark

6. 35% of 80 =

1 mark

7. 15% of 40 =

1 mark

8. 35% of 40 =

1 mark

Answers

WHOLE NUMBERS

1 Written addition 1

1. 64
2. 192
3. 197
4. 313
5. 412
6. 568
7. 780
8. 762

2 Written addition 2

1. 777
2. 1,052
3. 1,200
4. 1,202
5. 4,427
6. 6,728
7. 16,877
8. 32,414

3 Written subtraction 1

1. 39
2. 34
3. 48
4. 25
5. 628
6. 627
7. 191
8. 1,260

4 Written subtraction 2

1. 4,395
2. 3,194
3. 5,395
4. 7,089
5. 1,662
6. 3,571
7. 5,236
8. 17,655

5 Multiplying by 10, 100 and 1,000

1. 170
2. 7,560
3. 7,689,000
4. 549,000
5. 85,490
6. 6,064,000
7. 345,000
8. 648,000

6 Short multiplication 1

1. 78
2. 378
3. 801
4. 1,368
5. 2,280
6. 2,742
7. 6,264
8. 1,495

7 Short multiplication 2

1. 5,034
2. 13,390
3. 78,976
4. 23,975
5. 69,912
6. 36,715
7. 27,936
8. 32,592

8 Long multiplication 1

1. 264
2. 1,032
3. 2,128
4. 3,082
5. 10,286
6. 29,145

9 Long multiplication 2

1. 49,245
2. 93,096
3. 166,752
4. 353,790
5. 376,992
6. 174,384

10 Dividing by 10, 100 and 1,000

1. 4
2. 3
3. 14
4. 7
5. 25
6. 320
7. 172
8. 1

11 Short division

1. 24
2. 59
3. 73
4. 103

5. 132

6. 12

7. 52

8. 108

12 Short division with remainders

1. 20 r 2

2. 17 r 1

3. 14 r 2

4. 101 r 7

5. 63 r 8

6. 14 r 1

7. 72 r 1

8. 114 r 5

13 Long division

1. 12

2. 11

3. 32

4. 15

5. 15

6. 17

14 Long division with remainders

1. 12 r 1

2. 10 r 5

3. 21 r 9

4. 149 r 17

5. 121 r 27

6. 167 r 26

15 Squares and cubes

1. a) 9   b) 49   c) 64
   d) 121   e) 81   f) 144

2. a) 8   b) 27
   c) 729   d) 216

3. a) 72   b) 48

16 Mixed operations

1. a) 12   b) 6

2. a) 11   b) 21

3. a) 5   b) 45

4. a) 2   b) 4

5. a) 20   b) 12

DECIMALS

17 Adding decimals 1

1. 14

2. 14.4

3. 21.6

4. 34.1

5. 38.3

6. 52

7. 89.2

8. 55.2

18 Adding decimals 2

1. 85.36

2. 320.64

3. 851.66

4. 91.85

5. 200.11

6. 347.64

7. 261.42

8. 563.26

19 Subtracting decimals 1

1. 8.3

2. 3.64

3. 2.85

4. 19.15

5. 3.94

6. 47.51

7. 33.33

8. 48.89

20 Subtracting decimals 2

1. 59.03

2. 25.03

3. 16.21

4. 16.89

5. 29.32

6. 45.8

7. 73.98

8. 10.98

21 Multiplying decimals by 10, 100 and 1,000

1. 7.5

2. 750

3. 1,560

4. 95.2

5. 952

6. 9,520

7. 6,732

8. 5,102

22 Multiplying with decimals 1

1. 1.5

2. 28.02

3. 55.86

4. 78.03

5. 64.4

6. 41.15

7. 44.56

8. 61.02

23 Multiplying with decimals 2

1. 2

2. 4.9

3. 4.8

4. 0.06

Answers

5. 0.12
6. 0.12
7. 0.21
8. 0.24

24 Dividing by 10, 100 and 1,000 with decimals

1. 6.7
2. 0.893
3. 0.012
4. 1.97
5. 0.085
6. 98.95
7. 0.652
8. 4.02

25 Dividing with decimal answers 1

1. 6.5
2. 4.25
3. 24.5
4. 8.25
5. 231.2
6. 20.5
7. 292.5
8. 1,716.4

26 Dividing with decimal answers 2

1. 131.5
2. 48.2
3. 245.6
4. 101.25
5. 202.25
6. 96.25

FRACTIONS

27 Adding fractions

1. $\frac{7}{10}$
2. $\frac{3}{5}$
3. $\frac{5}{10}$ or $\frac{1}{2}$
4. $\frac{3}{9}$ or $\frac{1}{3}$
5. $\frac{4}{4}$ or 1
6. $\frac{4}{8}$ or $\frac{1}{2}$
7. $\frac{10}{12}$ or $\frac{5}{6}$
8. $\frac{5}{5}$ or 1

28 Adding fractions with different denominators

1. $\frac{3}{4}$
2. $\frac{3}{6}$ or $\frac{1}{2}$
3. $\frac{5}{10}$ or $\frac{1}{2}$

4. $\frac{8}{12}$ or $\frac{2}{3}$
5. $\frac{8}{15}$
6. $\frac{11}{24}$
7. $\frac{7}{10}$
8. $\frac{14}{15}$

29 Subtracting fractions

1. $\frac{3}{10}$
2. $\frac{2}{5}$
3. $\frac{4}{10}$ or $\frac{2}{5}$
4. $\frac{4}{8}$ or $\frac{1}{2}$
5. $\frac{6}{9}$ or $\frac{2}{3}$
6. $\frac{6}{10}$ or $\frac{3}{5}$
7. $\frac{2}{12}$ or $\frac{1}{6}$
8. $\frac{1}{5}$

30 Subtracting fractions with different denominators

1. $\frac{1}{4}$
2. $\frac{1}{6}$
3. $\frac{3}{10}$
4. $\frac{7}{15}$
5. $\frac{17}{40}$
6. $\frac{2}{15}$
7. $\frac{1}{12}$
8. $\frac{1}{10}$

31 Adding and subtracting with mixed numbers

1. $\frac{11}{4}$ or $2\frac{3}{4}$
2. $\frac{25}{6}$ or $4\frac{1}{6}$
3. $\frac{31}{24}$ or $1\frac{7}{24}$
4. $\frac{31}{10}$ or $3\frac{1}{10}$
5. $\frac{29}{12}$ or $2\frac{5}{12}$
6. $\frac{29}{10}$ or $2\frac{9}{10}$

32 Multiplying fractions 1

1. 1
2. $\frac{2}{3}$
3. 3
4. 4

41

5. $\frac{6}{5}$ or $1\frac{1}{5}$

6. $\frac{10}{6}$ or $\frac{5}{3}$ or $1\frac{2}{3}$

7. $\frac{20}{8}$ or $\frac{5}{2}$ or $2\frac{1}{2}$

8. $\frac{8}{3}$ or $2\frac{2}{3}$

33 Multiplying fractions 2

1. $\frac{1}{12}$

2. $\frac{20}{30}$ or $\frac{2}{3}$

3. $\frac{5}{40}$ or $\frac{1}{8}$

4. $\frac{6}{20}$ or $\frac{3}{10}$

5. $\frac{12}{40}$ or $\frac{3}{10}$

6. $\frac{14}{40}$ or $\frac{7}{20}$

7. $\frac{15}{40}$ or $\frac{3}{8}$

8. $\frac{6}{12}$ or $\frac{1}{2}$

34 Dividing fractions 1

1. $\frac{1}{12}$

2. $\frac{1}{15}$

3. $\frac{3}{16}$

4. $\frac{3}{20}$

5. $\frac{5}{18}$

6. $\frac{5}{24}$

7. $\frac{3}{20}$

8. $\frac{2}{15}$

35 Dividing fractions 2

1. $\frac{1}{30}$

2. $\frac{4}{50}$ or $\frac{2}{25}$

3. $\frac{5}{96}$

4. $\frac{3}{33}$ or $\frac{1}{11}$

5. $\frac{5}{168}$

6. $\frac{3}{240}$ or $\frac{1}{80}$

7. $\frac{7}{120}$

8. $\frac{7}{376}$

36 Multiplying and dividing with mixed numbers

1. $\frac{27}{4}$ or $6\frac{3}{4}$

2. $\frac{50}{3}$ or $16\frac{2}{3}$

3. $\frac{19}{16}$ or $1\frac{3}{16}$

4. $\frac{9}{20}$

5. $\frac{42}{4}$ or $\frac{21}{2}$ or $10\frac{1}{2}$

6. $18\frac{3}{4}$ or $18\frac{3}{8}$

PERCENTAGES

37 Percentage amounts 1

1. 6

2. 6

3. 6

4. 27

5. 12

6. 4

7. 40

8. 36

38 Percentage amounts 2

1. 1

2. 5

3. 3

4. 9

5. 4

6. 28

7. 6

8. 14

Published by Pearson Education Limited, 80 Strand, London, WC2R 0RL.

www.pearsonschools.co.uk

Text © Pearson Education Limited 2016
Edited by Christine Vaughan
Typeset by Jouve India Private Limited
Produced by Elektra Media
Original illustrations © Pearson Education Limited 2016
Illustrated by Elektra Media
Cover illustration by Ana Albero

The rights of Christopher Bishop and Brian Speed to be identified as authors of this work have been asserted by them in accordance with the Copyright, Designs and Patents Act 1988.

First published 2016

19 18 17 16
10 9 8 7 6 5 4 3 2 1

British Library Cataloguing in Publication Data
A catalogue record for this book is available from the British Library.

ISBN 978 1 292 14621 8

Printed in Italy by L.E.G.O. S.p.A. Lavis (TN)